THE MUSIC·MACHINE

A Musical Adventure Teaching the Fruit of the Spirit To All Ages

Choral arrangements by Jimmy Owens for Candle 🕯

Transcribèd and edited by Phil Perkins

**The Music Machine is performed by Candle on Birdwing Records (BWR-2004).
Also available: 8 track tape (BW8-2004); Cassette (BWC-2004);
Accompaniment tape (AT-505-B); Staging manual (SM-4).**

Edited by Milton Okun

ISBN 0-89524-079-3

© Birdwing Music 1977   All rights reserved   ASCAP

No part of this publication may be reproduced or transmitted in any form or by any means, electronic or mechanical, including photocopy, recording, or any information storage and retrieval system, without permisssion in writing from the publisher.

Birdwing Music, a division of Sparrow Records, Inc., Canoga Park, CA 91304

Printed in U.S.A.

INTRODUCTION

This dramatic musical work was born with the desire to reach into homes with the spiritual truth found in "the fruit of the Spirit." It was not originally conceived as a performing musical. When I heard the tape the first time I knew that with a little imagination this could be a very effective "teaching tool" for numerous combinations of musical groups in the local church.

After you listen to the record, read the musical score, and look at the incredible, illustrated book, I'm sure you will immediately have many ideas as to how to use this musical to make "The Music Machine" come alive. Here are a few quick ideas to get you started:

1. Stage the Conductor, Nancy, Stevie, and the Music Machine with the young singers of the church performing most of the music with occasional solos.

   Adapt many of the solos by older singers on the recording to your local situation.

2. Create "puppets" in the form of the characters of the musical and let soloists and young singing groups perform from behind stage or to the side of the puppets.

3. Do a complete staging of the score using adults, young people, and young singers to perform just as the recording is done.

4. Do combinations of all of the above.

However you decide to use it in your church, do everything you can to get an album
with the illustrated book into as many homes as possible.
This will accomplish the original purpose of the composing, recording, and illustrating of this work —
to teach the fruit of the Spirit in thousands of homes.

Billy Ray Hearn

CONTENTS

A Land Called Love

Words and Music by
FRANK HERNANDEZ and
SHERRY SAUNDERS

Love is real and love is

© Copyright 1977 Sparrow Song/Candle Company Music/World Artist Music Co., Inc.
All rights throughout the world administered by World Artist Music Co., Inc.
International Copyright Secured   All Rights Reserved

The Music Machine

JIM and DEE PATTON,
FRANK HERNANDEZ and
MIKE MILLIGAN

JIM and DEE PATTON,
FRANK HERNANDEZ

© Copyright 1977 Sparrow Song/Candle Company Music/World Artist Music Co., Inc.
All rights throughout the world administered by World Artist Music Co., Inc.
International Copyright Secured   All Rights Reserved

Whistle Song

Words and Music by
FRANK HERNANDEZ and
SHERRY SAUNDERS

1. God made the birds to whis-tle in tune___ songs in the morn and the
2. Hot steam-y ket-tles whis-tle a song,___ fast mov-in' trains as they're

© Copyright 1977 Sparrow Song/Candle Company Music/World Artist Music Co., Inc.
All rights throughout the world administered by World Artist Music Co., Inc.
International Copyright Secured   All Rights Reserved

aft - er - noon;__ e - ven at night you can hear them sing__
chug-gin' a - long.__ Lis - ten and hear in__ ev - 'ry - thing__

songs of praise to the King of Kings.__ *Whistle*
songs of praise to the King of Kings.__

(whistle)

(whistle)

Smile

GEORGIAN BANOV and
WINNIE COOK

GEORGIAN BANOV

1. Smile, smile, smile, I____ love to smile.
2. Smile, smile, smile, all cre-a-tion smiles.
3. Smile, smile, smile, God____ loves to smile.

E-ven when tears in my eyes____ ap-
An-i-mals too, mon-keys and____ kan-ga-
He loves us oh, do you know?____ do you

pear, in a lit-tle while
roos. E-ven croc-o-diles
know? He____ loves us so,

© Copyright 1977 Sparrow Song/Candle Company Music/World Artist Music Co., Inc.
All rights throughout the world administered by World Artist Music Co., Inc.
International Copyright Secured   All Rights Reserved

* Italicized words are to be spoken.

The String Song

Words and Music by
MARK PENDERGRASS

© Copyright 1977 Sparrow Song/ Candle Company Music/ World Artist Music Co., Inc.
All rights throughout the world administered by World Artist Music Co., Inc.
International Copyright Secured   All Rights Reserved

Patience

Words and Music by
FRANK HERNANDEZ and
SHERRY SAUNDERS

© Copyright 1977 Sparrow Song/Candle Company Music/World Artist Music Co., Inc.
All rights throughout the world administered by World Artist Music Co., Inc.
International Copyright Secured   All Rights Reserved

times when oth-ers have to wait for you. 2. When you.

3. As you can well im-ag-ine, there's a mor-al to this tale.

slide
whistle

Some of you may find your-selves be-hind a creep-ing snail. So if you are im-

pa-tient and you're eas-i-ly dis-turbed, think a-bout this lit-tle song and

Gentleness

**GEORGIAN BANOV
and WINNIE COOK**

GEORGIAN BANOV

1. Gen-tle___ breeze, gen - tle___ breeze blow - ing when___ you
(2.) still of___ the___ night when___ you
(3.) Son walked___ the___ earth, He___ was

© Copyright 1977 Sparrow Song/Candle Company Music/World Artist Music Co., Inc.
All rights throughout the world administered by World Artist Music Co., Inc.
International Copyright Secured   All Rights Reserved

Faith

Words and Music by
FRANK HERNANDEZ and
SHERRY SAUNDERS

© Copyright 1977 Sparrow Song/Candle Company Music/World Artist Music Co., Inc.
All rights throughout the world administered by World Artist Music Co., Inc.
International Copyright Secured   All Rights Reserved

Joy

Words and Music by
JIM and DEE PATTON

1. Joy   from me,   joy   from you,   joy   is   some - thing
2. Give   a - way   pure   de - light,   make   some - one

that   we   do.   Joy   to   me,   joy   to   you,___ and
feel   all   right.   That's   what   joy   real - ly   is,___ let's

*Cue notes indicate optional harmony. Second time only.

© Copyright 1977 Sparrow Song/Candle Company Music/World Artist Music Co., Inc.
All rights throughout the world administered by World Artist Music Co., Inc.
International Copyright Secured   All Rights Reserved

learn   to give._____

Peace

Words and Music by
WAYNE ZEITNER

1. Peace is when the wind stops blow-ing, peace is where the sun is show-ing,
2. Peace is when I'm tucked in bed, when my mom-my pats my head;

© Copyright 1977 Sparrow Song/Candle Company Music/World Artist Music Co., Inc.
All rights throughout the world administered by World Artist Music Co., Inc.
International Copyright Secured   All Rights Reserved

Goodness

Words and Music by
MIKE MILLIGAN

© Copyright 1977 Sparrow Song/Candle Company Music/World Artist Music Co., Inc.
All rights throughout the world administered by World Artist Music Co., Inc.
International Copyright Secured   All Rights Reserved

Love

Words and Music by
FRANK HERNANDEZ and
SHERRY SAUNDERS

1. Love, love, love makes peo-ple hap - py;____
2. Love, love, love makes peo-ple friend - ly;____
3. Love, love, love makes peo-ple thank-ful;____

love, love, love makes peo - ple free.____   Love makes peo-ple do____ the
love, love, love makes peo - ple kind.____   Love makes peo-ple do____ the
love, love, love makes peo - ple share.____   Love makes peo-ple do____ the

* Optional introduction

© Copyright 1977 Sparrow Song/Candle Company Music/World Artist Music Co., Inc.
All rights throughout the world administered by World Artist Music Co., Inc.
International Copyright Secured   All Rights Reserved

Self-Control

Words and Music by
MIKE MILLIGAN

1. Once I had a knot in my shoe and it would not come loose. I tried and tried and tried and tried, but it would not come loose. I got so mad I kicked the door____ and

(2.) nev - er liked to brush__my teeth, I wished that I could stop. I'd have more time for can - dy bars and drink - ing so - da pop. But soon my teeth would hurt so bad____ from

© Copyright 1977 Sparrow Song/Candle Company Music/World Artist Music Co., Inc.
All rights throughout the world administered by World Artist Music Co., Inc.
International Copyright Secured   All Rights Reserved

30

D   G   D

smart.   Self   con -   trol   is the

F#   Bm   A7

ver - y best way to go_____ so I think that I'll_____ con -

35

A6   A7   **1** D

trol   my -   self.

D   **2** D

2. I   self.

Kindness

GEORGIAN BANOV
and WINNIE COOK

GEORGIAN BANOV

1. When I treat you kind - ly, it makes you hap - py,
(2.) treat you kind - ly, it makes you thank - ful,

chang - es you in - side, makes you feel im - por - tant,
chang - es you in - side, makes you feel en - cour - aged,

© Copyright 1977 Sparrow Song/Candle Company Music/World Artist Music Co., Inc.
All rights throughout the world administered by World Artist Music Co., Inc.
International Copyright Secured   All Rights Reserved

44

The Music Machine
(REPRISE)

JIM and DEE PATTON,
FRANK HERNANDEZ and
MIKE MILLIGAN

JIM and DEE PATTON
FRANK HERNANDEZ

Mu-sic ma-chine, ___ mu-sic ma-chine ___ like no oth-er gad-get that you've ev-er seen. ___ What-ev-er you want ___ to sing ___ a-bout, ___ put some-thing in ___ it and a song ___ comes out.

© Copyright 1977 Sparrow Song/Candle Company Music/World Artist Music Co., Inc.
All rights throughout the world administered by World Artist Music Co., Inc.
International Copyright Secured   All Rights Reserved

Music Typeset by
VICTOR L. GUMMA
Dallas, Texas

DIALOGUE

Song:	"LAND CALLED LOVE"
Stevie:	Oh, what happened, Nancy?
Nancy:	I don't know, Stevie. Where are we?
Stevie:	I'm not sure, but it's so pretty.
Nancy:	I've never seen anything like this before.
Conductor:	Hello there, Stevie and Nancy.
Stevie & Nancy:	Who are you?
Conductor:	I'm the conductor here in Agapeland.
Stevie:	Agapeland, where's that?
Conductor:	Oh, it's a pretty good ways from where you live, I guess. But then again, not as far as you might think.
Stevie:	What do you do?
Conductor:	Well, I do a lot of things.
Nancy:	Stevie, look over there.
Stevie:	What's that?
Conductor:	That? Why, that's the Music Machine.
Song:	"THE MUSIC MACHINE"
Conductor:	I can put something in it, and a song will come out. Take, for instance, my whistle.
Song:	"WHISTLE SONG"
Stevie:	Look, the Music Machine gave the whistle back.
Nancy:	Wow! I wish I had something to put into the Machine.
Conductor:	You do have something.
Nancy:	I do?
Conductor:	Sure, what about that smile. Why don't you look into the slot on the Machine and smile real big.
Nancy:	Okay.
Song:	"SMILE"
Nancy:	That was beautiful!
Stevie:	Hey, watch this. I'm gonna try this piece of string.
Song:	"THE STRING SONG"
Conductor:	There are many things that we can learn from the Music Machine. Would you like to hear more?
Stevie:	Oh, may we?
Conductor:	Yes, yes. I'll tell you what. I'm going to put in something very special, and let's see what comes out.
Nancy:	What is it?

Conductor:	It's a little quote from the Bible — about fruit.
Nancy:	You mean apples and bananas?
Conductor:	Well, not exactly, Nancy. This verse is about a different kind of fruit. Things like love and joy; peace, patience, kindness, gentleness, goodness, faith, and self-control.
Stevie:	Wow! I'd like to see what would come out if you put all those in.
Conductor:	Ready? Here we go.
Song:	"PATIENCE"
Song:	"GENTLENESS"
Conductor:	Well, how do you like it so far?
Nancy:	Wow! Now I think I'm starting to see what you mean about fruit.
Stevie:	Yeah, and I bet we could grow some of this kind of fruit at our house
Conductor:	Wait, that's not all. Let's get the Machine going again.
Song:	"FAITH"
Song:	"JOY"
Nancy:	I never knew that joy could be given away.
Stevie:	Hey, here comes another song.
Song:	"PEACE"
Song:	"GOODNESS"
Song:	"LOVE"
Conductor:	Well, how are we doing?
Stevie:	Oh, great! There's been patience, gentleness, faith, and joy; peace, goodness, and love.
Nancy:	Wow! That's one, two, three, four, five, six, and seven. Are there anymore?
Conductor:	Yes, hold on. There are two more. That makes nine in all. Here we go again.
Song:	"SELF-CONTROL"
Song:	"KINDNESS"
Conductor:	Well, Stevie and Nancy, I think the time has come for you to go back. It's been good to have you here.
Stevie & Nancy:	Thank you!
Stevie:	Good-bye, Mr. Conductor!
Nancy:	Good-bye, Music Machine!
Stevie & Nancy:	Good-bye!
Conductor:	Yes, yes, good-bye, children. You'll be back.
Song:	"REPRISE"